SECURE

A QUICK GUIDE TO STOWAGE, LASHING, AND SECURING CARGO

Disclaimer: The information presented here is for informational and educational purposes only. It does not construe professional advice. You assume the sole responsibility of relying on this information at your own risk.

Published by
Baumgartner & Moreira Lda.
Rua Eng Maia Bernardo 101
4435-224 Rio Tinto
Portugal

app.cargobid.org

TABLE OF CONTENTS

CARGOBID
BASICS

MESSAGE
FROM AUTHOR

Shipping your goods in the global trade brings challenges when it comes to ensuring the safe handling, transport and delivery of cargo. Safety depends from the outset on a proper setup across all steps of supply chains.

We hope this short handbook can help you deal with some of those factors in your operations.

Carlos Moreira

Founder, CargoBid

What is CargoBid?

A leading global provider of freight auctions, offering a cool experience for multimodal freight. Post auctions. Make bids. Close deals. Join us at app.cargobid.org

INTRODUCTION TO STOWAGE, LASHING, AND SECURING CARGO

The transport of goods is an essential aspect of global trade and commerce. In today's world, goods are transported across the world through various modes of transportation, including sea, air, and land. The safe and secure transportation of cargo is of utmost importance, not just for the protection of the goods but also for the safety of those involved in the transportation process. This is where stowage, lashing, and securing cargo come into play.

Stowage, lashing, and securing cargo are the processes of properly arranging cargo within the transportation vessel and securing it with the use of lashing equipment. These processes ensure that the cargo remains safe and secure during transportation, preventing damage to the goods and avoiding accidents that could cause injury or loss of life.

Proper stowage, lashing, and securing of cargo require knowledge and expertise in various areas, such as cargo characteristics, stowage methods, lashing techniques, and safety regulations. It is essential to choose the right stowage method, lashing equipment, and securing methods to ensure the safe transportation of cargo, no matter the mode of transportation.

In this handbook, we will delve into the intricacies of stowage, lashing, and securing cargo, exploring the principles, techniques, and equipment involved. We will also discuss the challenges and solutions involved in this process, as well as best practices to ensure the safe transportation of cargo. Whether you are involved in the transportation of goods or simply interested in the subject, this ebook will provide you with a comprehensive understanding of stowage, lashing, and securing cargo, and the importance of these processes in global trade and commerce.

TYPES OF CARGO AND THEIR CHARACTERISTICS

When it comes to stowage, lashing, and securing cargo, understanding the types of cargo being transported is essential. Each cargo type has unique characteristics that require specific stowage and securing methods to ensure safe transportation. In this article, we will explore the different types of cargo and their characteristics.

General Cargo

General cargo includes goods that are packaged, palletized, or bundled, such as consumer goods, machinery, and equipment. General cargo can be further classified into breakbulk cargo, which is handled individually, and containerized cargo, which is transported in standardized containers. General cargo is characterized by its diverse nature, weight, and size, which require proper stowage and securing methods, such as cross-bracing, lashing, and dunnage.

Bulk Cargo

Bulk cargo refers to goods that are transported unpackaged, such as grain, coal, and ore. Bulk cargo is characterized by its weight and volume, which require specific stowage methods, such as stacking, trimming, and segregation. The stowage of bulk cargo must also take into consideration the cargo's characteristics, such as flow properties and potential for shifting, which can affect the stability of the transportation vessel.

CARGOBID
BASICS

Hazardous Cargo

Hazardous cargo includes goods that are potentially dangerous or harmful, such as chemicals, explosives, and radioactive materials. Hazardous cargo is characterized by its specific transportation regulations, labeling requirements, and safety precautions. The stowage and securing of hazardous cargo require specific equipment, such as specialized containers, and adherence to safety regulations and procedures, such as proper ventilation and firefighting systems.

Refrigerated Cargo

Refrigerated cargo includes goods that require temperature-controlled transportation, such as perishable food items, pharmaceuticals, and vaccines. Refrigerated cargo is characterized by its specific temperature and humidity requirements, which must be maintained throughout transportation. The stowage and securing of refrigerated cargo require specialized equipment, such as refrigerated containers, and adherence to temperature and humidity regulations and procedures.

Oversized Cargo

Oversized cargo includes goods that are too large or heavy to be transported in standard containers, such as machinery, equipment, and vehicles. Oversized cargo is characterized by its unique shape, size, and weight, which require specialized stowage and securing methods, such as platform stowage, tie-downs, and custom-made transport containers.

Understanding the different types of cargo and their characteristics is essential for safe and secure transportation. Proper stowage and securing methods must be employed to ensure the safe transportation of cargo, no matter the type. By taking into consideration the cargo's characteristics, such as weight, size, and potential hazards, and utilizing appropriate stowage and securing methods, cargo can be transported safely and efficiently, contributing to the success of global trade and commerce.

CARGOBID
BASICS

PRINCIPLES OF STOWAGE

The safe transportation of cargo requires proper stowage principles to ensure the cargo remains secure and stable throughout the transportation process. The principles of stowage involve the proper arrangement of cargo within the transportation vessel to ensure its weight is distributed evenly and secured in place. In this article, we will explore the principles of stowage.

Center of Gravity

The center of gravity of the cargo must be taken into consideration when stowing the cargo. The center of gravity is the point at which the cargo's weight is evenly distributed. The cargo's center of gravity must be aligned with the centerline of the transportation vessel to ensure its stability during transportation.

Weight Distribution

The weight distribution of the cargo must be evenly spread throughout the transportation vessel to prevent any shift in weight that could cause instability. Heavy items should be placed at the bottom of the stowage, and lighter items should be placed on top. The weight distribution should also take into consideration the vessel's capacity and stability.

CARGOBID
BASICS

Cargo Securing

The cargo must be secured in place to prevent any movement during transportation. Cargo securing methods include lashing, dunnage, and cross-bracing. The cargo securing equipment must be capable of withstanding the weight and force of the cargo and must be inspected regularly to ensure its integrity.

Separation

Cargo should be separated according to its characteristics, such as hazardous materials, temperature-controlled cargo, and oversized cargo. Separation prevents potential hazards and damage to the cargo during transportation. Cargo should also be separated by weight and size to ensure the stability of the transportation vessel.

Ventilation

The transportation vessel must be properly ventilated to prevent the build-up of moisture, heat, and gases that could damage the cargo. The ventilation system should be inspected regularly to ensure it is functioning correctly.

CARGOBID
BASICS

Trim and List

The transportation vessel must be trimmed and listed to ensure the cargo remains stable during transportation. Trim refers to the balance of the vessel's weight between the forward and aft. List refers to the balance of the vessel's weight between the port and starboard. The vessel must be trimmed and listed according to the cargo's weight and distribution.

As we can see, the principles of stowage involve the proper arrangement of cargo within the transportation vessel to ensure its weight is distributed evenly and secured in place. The center of gravity, weight distribution, cargo securing, separation, ventilation, and trim and list must all be taken into consideration to ensure safe and secure transportation of cargo. By adhering to these principles, cargo can be transported efficiently and effectively, contributing to the success of global trade and commerce.

CARGOBID
BASICS

CHOOSING THE RIGHT STOWAGE METHOD

Choosing the most adequate stowage method is crucial for the safe and efficient transportation of cargo. The stowage method depends on various factors, such as the type of cargo, transportation mode, and destination. In this article, we will discuss the different stowage methods and how to choose the right one for your cargo.

Flat Stowage

Flat stowage is the most common stowage method, and it involves placing cargo on the vessel's floor. This method is suitable for heavy cargo, such as machinery and equipment. Flat stowage allows for easy loading and unloading of cargo, and it maximizes the vessel's storage capacity. However, flat stowage can be challenging to secure, and cargo may shift during transportation, causing instability.

Vertical Stowage

Vertical stowage involves stacking cargo on top of each other in a vertical position. This method is suitable for lightweight cargo, such as vehicles, and it maximizes the vessel's storage capacity. However, vertical stowage can be challenging to secure, and cargo may shift during transportation, causing instability.

Cellular Stowage

Cellular stowage involves dividing the vessel's cargo hold into compartments using bulkheads. This method is suitable for a variety of cargo types and ensures the cargo remains secure and stable during transportation. Cellular stowage allows for easy access to the cargo and facilitates efficient loading and unloading. However, cellular stowage can reduce the vessel's storage capacity, and it can be challenging to load oversized cargo.

Ro-Ro Stowage

Ro-Ro stowage involves rolling cargo on and off the vessel using a ramp. This method is suitable for wheeled cargo, such as cars and trucks. Ro-Ro stowage allows for easy loading and unloading of cargo, and it maximizes the vessel's storage capacity. However, Ro-Ro stowage can be expensive, and it requires specialized equipment and facilities.

Containerized Stowage

Containerized stowage involves loading cargo into containers, which are then loaded onto the vessel. This method is suitable for a variety of cargo types and ensures the cargo remains secure and stable during transportation. Containerized stowage allows for efficient loading and unloading, and it facilitates intermodal transportation. However, containerized stowage can be expensive, and it requires specialized equipment and facilities.

To choose the right stowage method, consider the type of cargo, transportation mode, and destination. It's essential to ensure the stowage method is compatible with the cargo's characteristics and transportation requirements. It's also important to consider the cost and availability of the stowage method and the required equipment and facilities.

In conclusion, choosing the right stowage method is crucial for the safe and efficient transportation of cargo. Flat stowage, vertical stowage, cellular stowage, Ro-Ro stowage, and containerized stowage are the most common stowage methods. By considering the type of cargo, transportation mode, and destination, and weighing the advantages and disadvantages of each stowage method, you can choose the most suitable method for your cargo.

CARGOBID
BASICS

PREPARING FOR LASHING AND SECURING CARGO

Lashing and securing cargo is essential for the safe transportation of goods. Proper preparation is key to ensuring that cargo is secured correctly and does not shift during transportation. In this article, we will discuss the steps involved in preparing for lashing and securing cargo.

CARGOBID
BASICS

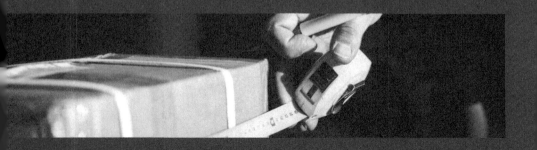

Determine the Type of Cargo

The first step in preparing for lashing and securing cargo is to determine the type of cargo. Different types of cargo require different lashing and securing techniques. For example, heavy machinery requires different securing methods than lightweight cargo. Understanding the cargo's characteristics and requirements will help in selecting the appropriate lashing and securing techniques.

Choose the Right Equipment

Once you have determined the type of cargo, you need to choose the right equipment for lashing and securing. The equipment can include ropes, chains, webbing, and shackles. It is essential to use equipment that is strong enough to secure the cargo and is in good condition. Damaged or worn-out equipment can compromise the safety of the cargo during transportation.

CARGOBID
BASICS

Calculate the Required Tension

The next step in preparing for lashing and securing cargo is to calculate the required tension. The tension is the force applied to the cargo to hold it securely in place during transportation. The required tension depends on the cargo's weight, size, and transportation mode. It is essential to calculate the required tension to ensure that the cargo is secured correctly and does not shift during transportation.

Choose the Right Lashing and Securing Technique

There are different lashing and securing techniques, including direct lashing, diagonal lashing, and vertical lashing. The choice of the lashing and securing technique depends on the cargo's weight, size, and transportation mode. It is essential to choose the appropriate technique to ensure that the cargo is secured correctly and does not shift during transportation.

CARGOBID
BASICS

Inspect the Cargo and Equipment

Before lashing and securing the cargo, it is important to inspect the cargo and equipment. Inspecting the cargo ensures that it is stable and will not shift during transportation. Inspecting the equipment ensures that it is in good condition and can withstand the required tension. It is essential to inspect both the cargo and equipment to ensure that the lashing and securing process is successful.

The truth of the matter is preparing for lashing and securing cargo is crucial for the safe transportation of goods. The steps involved in preparing for lashing and securing cargo include determining the type of cargo, choosing the right equipment, calculating the required tension, choosing the right lashing and securing technique, and inspecting the cargo and equipment.
By following these steps, you can ensure that the cargo is secured correctly and does not shift during transportation, ensuring the safety of the cargo and the transportation crew.

CARGOBID
BASICS

TYPES OF LASHING EQUIPMENT

Lashing equipment is essential for securing cargo during transportation. There are different types of lashing equipment available in the market, each designed for a specific purpose. In this article, we will discuss the types of lashing equipment used in securing cargo.

Ratchet Straps

Ratchet straps are one of the most commonly used lashing equipment. They are designed to secure cargo using a ratcheting mechanism that tightens the strap around the cargo. The straps are made of strong materials such as nylon, polyester, or polypropylene and are available in various lengths and widths.

Chains

Chains are another common lashing equipment used for securing heavy cargo. They are made of durable materials such as steel or alloy and are available in various lengths and thicknesses. Chains are ideal for securing cargo that requires high tension.

Webbing Straps

Webbing straps are similar to ratchet straps but are made of flat woven materials such as nylon or polyester. They are lightweight and ideal for securing cargo that requires low to medium tension. They are available in various lengths and widths.

Rope

Rope is a traditional lashing equipment that is still widely used in securing cargo. They are made of natural fibers such as hemp or synthetic materials such as nylon or polyester. Ropes are available in various sizes and strengths and are ideal for securing lightweight cargo.

Steel Wire Rope

Steel wire rope is a heavy-duty lashing equipment designed to secure heavy cargo. They are made of high-strength steel wires twisted together to form a rope. Steel wire ropes are available in various diameters and strengths and are ideal for securing cargo that requires high tension.

Turnbuckles

Turnbuckles are lashing equipment used to adjust tension in the securing process. They are made of steel or alloy and consist of two threaded eye bolts connected by a central body. Turnbuckles are ideal for securing cargo that requires adjustable tension.

Ultimately, lashing equipment is crucial for securing cargo during transportation. The types of lashing equipment available include ratchet straps, chains, webbing straps, ropes, steel wire ropes, and turnbuckles. Choosing the appropriate lashing equipment depends on the cargo's weight, size, and transportation mode. It is essential to select the appropriate lashing equipment to ensure that the cargo is secured correctly and does not shift during transportation, ensuring the safety of the cargo and the transportation crew.

CARGOBID
BASICS

LASHING TECHNIQUES

Lashing techniques are essential for securing cargo during transportation. Improperly secured cargo can cause accidents, injuries, and damage to the cargo and transportation equipment. Therefore, it is crucial to use the correct lashing technique and equipment for different types of cargo. In this article, we will discuss the different lashing techniques used to secure cargo.

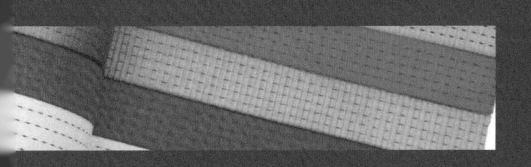

Cross Lashing

Cross lashing is a commonly used technique for securing cargo in containers. It involves using lashing equipment such as ropes or chains to secure the cargo diagonally from one corner to another. This technique helps to distribute the weight of the cargo evenly and prevent it from shifting during transportation.

Loop Lashing

Loop lashing is a technique used to secure cylindrical objects such as pipes or drums. It involves using lashing equipment to create a loop around the object and securing it to the transportation equipment. This technique helps to prevent the cylindrical object from rolling or shifting during transportation.

Vertical Lashing

Vertical lashing is a technique used to secure cargo that is taller than it is wide, such as machinery or equipment. It involves using lashing equipment to secure the cargo vertically to the transportation equipment. This technique helps to prevent the cargo from tipping over during transportation.

Friction Lashing

Friction lashing is a technique used to secure cargo that is already in contact with the transportation equipment, such as pallets or crates. It involves using lashing equipment to create friction between the cargo and the transportation equipment, preventing the cargo from shifting during transportation.

Direct Lashing

Direct lashing is a technique used to secure heavy cargo such as machinery or vehicles. It involves using lashing equipment such as chains or ropes to secure the cargo directly to the transportation equipment. This technique helps to distribute the weight of the cargo evenly and prevent it from shifting during transportation.

In conclusion, lashing techniques are crucial for securing cargo during transportation. The type of lashing technique used depends on the cargo's size, weight, and transportation mode. Cross lashing, loop lashing, vertical lashing, friction lashing, and direct lashing are some of the commonly used lashing techniques. It is essential to use the appropriate lashing technique and equipment to ensure that the cargo is secured correctly and does not shift during transportation, ensuring the safety of the cargo and the transportation crew.

CARGOBID
BASICS

SECURING CARGO ON DIFFERENT MODES OF TRANSPORTATION

Securing cargo on different modes of transportation is a critical aspect of logistics and transportation management. Proper cargo securing ensures the safety of the goods being transported, minimizes the risk of damage, and maintains the integrity of the supply chain. The methods and techniques for securing cargo can vary depending on the mode of transportation, which includes land, air, and sea. Here's an overview of cargo securing for each of these modes:

1. Land Transportation (Trucking and Rail)

Load Restraints
In trucking and rail transport, cargo is secured using load restraints such as straps, chains, and binders. These are used to prevent the cargo from shifting during transit.

Dunnage and Bracing
Dunnage materials like wooden blocks and bracing structures help in preventing the cargo from moving and shifting within the trailer or railcar.

Palletization
Placing goods on pallets or in containers can make it easier to secure the cargo and reduce the risk of damage during transportation.

Strapping and Tarping
Cargo can be secured with straps and tarps to protect it from the elements and prevent shifting.

2. Air Transportation

Air Cargo Containers
Cargo is typically loaded into standardized air cargo containers or Unit Load Devices (ULDs) that are designed to fit securely in the aircraft's cargo hold.

Netting and Tie-Downs

Cargo within ULDs is further secured with netting and tie-downs to prevent movement during turbulence or rapid maneuvers.

Shock and Vibration Absorption

Sensitive or fragile cargo may require shock-absorbing materials and specialized packaging to withstand the stresses of air travel.

3. Sea Transportation

Containerization

Cargo is packed into standardized shipping containers, which are then loaded onto vessels. Containerization provides a high level of security and prevents shifting during the voyage.

Blocking and Bracing

Within containers, cargo is secured with blocking and bracing materials, such as wood, to prevent movement.

Lashing and Chocking

On open decks, cargo is secured with lashing systems, including chains and cables. Chocking involves placing wooden wedges or chocks around cargo to prevent shifting.

Weather Protection

Cargo on ships is exposed to harsh weather conditions, so it's crucial to protect it from moisture and sea spray, often by using waterproof coverings.

General Cargo Securing Practices

Weight Distribution
Proper weight distribution is critical. Cargo should be evenly distributed to prevent overloading one side of the transport vehicle or container.

Brake and Suspension Systems
Ensure that the transport vehicle's brake and suspension systems are in good working condition to prevent cargo shifting due to sudden stops or bumps.

Regulatory Compliance
Different modes of transportation have specific regulations and guidelines for cargo securing. Compliance with these regulations is essential to ensure safety and avoid legal issues.

Regular Inspection
Periodic inspections during transportation are essential to check the integrity of cargo securing measures.

Securing cargo is a complex and vital aspect of transportation logistics. The choice of securing methods depends on the nature of the cargo, the mode of transportation, and regulatory requirements. When done correctly, it reduces the risk of damage, maintains supply chain integrity, and ensures the safe delivery of goods to their destination.

SAFETY CONSIDERATIONS FOR STOWAGE, LASHING, AND SECURING

Safety considerations for stowage, lashing, and securing cargo are of paramount importance in the transportation industry. The goal is not only to protect the cargo but also to ensure the safety of personnel involved in the loading and unloading process, as well as the safety of other road, air, or maritime users. Here are key safety considerations to keep in mind:

1. Personnel Safety

Proper Training: Ensure that all personnel involved in stowage, lashing, and securing operations are adequately trained in safe practices, including the use of equipment and proper lifting techniques.

Personal Protective Equipment (PPE)
Workers should wear appropriate PPE, such as gloves, safety boots, helmets, and high-visibility vests to reduce the risk of injury.

Avoid Overexertion
Prevent manual handling injuries by using equipment like forklifts or cranes for heavy or awkwardly shaped cargo.

2. Hazardous Materials

Identification
Clearly label and identify hazardous materials, and follow specific safety guidelines for their handling, containment, and stowage.

Segregation
Keep incompatible hazardous materials separated to prevent chemical reactions.

CARGOBID
BASICS

3. Equipment Safety

Equipment Inspection
Regularly inspect and maintain lashing and securing equipment to ensure it's in proper working condition.

Safe Usage
Train operators in the safe use of securing equipment to prevent accidents caused by misuse.

4. Weight Limits and Load Capacity

Weight Limits
Do not exceed weight limits set by the mode of transportation or equipment being used.

Load Center
Ensure that the cargo's weight is distributed evenly within the load center.

5. Stability and Balance

Load Distribution
Maintain a balanced and stable load distribution to prevent toppling, especially for top-heavy or tall cargo.

Center of Gravity
Understand the center of gravity for different types of cargo and ensure that it is properly located.

6. Weather and Environmental Conditions

Wind and Weather
Be mindful of weather conditions that could affect cargo stability and adjust securing measures as needed.

Moisture Protection
n maritime transport, protect cargo from exposure to saltwater, rain, or moisture

.

7. Regulatory Compliance

Know and Follow Regulations
Comply with regulations and guidelines specific to the mode of transportation, including weight restrictions, load securement rules, and hazardous materials handling requirements.

8. Emergency Response

Emergency Procedures
Develop and communicate emergency response procedures in the event of accidents or incidents that compromise cargo security.

CARGOBID
BASICS

9. Continuous Monitoring

In-Transit Checks
Continuously monitor the cargo during transit for signs of shifting, damage, or other issues that could affect safety.

10. Risk Assessment

Risk Evaluation
Conduct a comprehensive risk assessment to identify potential safety hazards associated with the cargo, transport mode, and route.

11. Communication

Clear Communication
Establish clear communication protocols between personnel involved in cargo handling and securing to prevent accidents due to misunderstandings or miscommunication.

Safety considerations are non-negotiable when it comes to stowage, lashing, and securing cargo. By prioritizing safety, you not only protect the cargo but also ensure the well-being of those involved in the process and maintain the safety of everyone on the road, in the air, or at sea. Safety should be an integral part of all cargo management processes.

CHALLENGES AND SOLUTIONS

Stowage, lashing, and securing cargo present several challenges that, if not addressed properly, can result in damage to the cargo, safety risks, and even legal issues. Here are some common challenges and their corresponding solutions:

1. Challenge: Varying Cargo Types and Sizes

Solution: Flexibility in Securing

- Use versatile securing equipment such as adjustable straps and modular securing systems to accommodate different cargo types and sizes.
- Train personnel to adapt to the unique requirements of each cargo load, understanding that one approach may not fit all situations.

2. Challenge: Hazardous Materials

Solution: Proper Handling and Labeling

- Comply with strict regulations for transporting hazardous materials.
- Clearly label hazardous materials, segregate incompatible substances, and provide proper containment for leaks or spills.

3. Challenge: Inadequate Training and Competence

Solution: Education and Training

- Invest in continuous training for personnel involved in cargo securing, ensuring they are up-to-date with safety regulations and best practices.
- Regularly assess their competence and provide feedback and reinforcement when needed.

4. Challenge: Equipment Failure

Solution: Maintenance and Inspection

- Implement a rigorous maintenance and inspection schedule for all lashing and securing equipment.
- Replace worn-out or damaged equipment promptly to prevent accidents or cargo damage.

5. Challenge: Weather Conditions

Solution: Weatherproofing

- Use weather-resistant materials for cargo securing, including straps, tarps, and containers.
- Monitor weather conditions and adapt securing measures accordingly. Delay transport if conditions are unsafe.

6. Challenge: Weight Distribution and Balance

Solution: Load Planning

- Use load planning software to ensure proper weight distribution and cargo balance.
- Train personnel to understand the center of gravity for different types of cargo and the importance of proper load placement.

7. Challenge: Emergency Situations

Solution: Emergency Response Protocols

- Develop and communicate emergency response protocols to address accidents, shifting cargo, or other incidents.
- Train personnel on how to respond to various emergency scenarios and have appropriate emergency equipment on hand.

8. Challenge: Regulatory Compliance

Solution: Stay Informed and Compliant

- Keep up-to-date with the latest regulations and guidelines for cargo securing in your specific mode of transportation.
- Conduct regular audits to ensure compliance with these regulations and adjust procedures as necessary.

9. Challenge: Communication

Solution: Clear Communication

- Establish clear communication channels between all personnel involved in cargo handling and securing.
- Ensure that everyone understands their roles and responsibilities and can communicate effectively, especially in high-pressure situations.

CARGOBID
BASICS

10. Challenge: Lack of Real-time Monitoring

Solution: Real-time Tracking and Monitoring

- Invest in tracking and monitoring technology that allows for real-time assessment of cargo security during transit.
- Implement remote monitoring systems that can alert operators to any issues or irregularities.

Dealing with challenges related to stowage, lashing, and securing cargo requires a combination of effective training, adherence to regulations, and adaptability in the face of varying cargo types and environmental conditions. By implementing these solutions, you can minimize the risks associated with cargo securing and ensure the safe and efficient transportation of goods.

CARGOBID
BASICS

ANNEX 1

CONTAINER GUIDE

Although it might not be suitable for all kinds of cargo, containerization has introduced a whole range of benefits. One of the main advantages is the cost savings that it offers for both shippers and carriers. Not only it provides lower handling costs, but it also reduces fuel consumption and transit times. Containerization has had a great impact in the globalization of international trade, particularly because the great variety of shipping containers sizes and dimensions allowed the intermodality of freight transportation.

Seashipping containers

Shippers need to consider the weight, total size and cargo unit packaging before choosing an appropriate container for their cargo. The origin and destination of the cargo, and the route in-between, also influence the kind of logistics necessary to complete a successful shipment operation in containers. The below table provides measurements for the most commonly used shipping containers.

20' Standard Dry	5.440 m 17'10 3/16"	2.294 m 7'6 1/4"	2.237 m 7'4 1/16"	27.9 m3 986 cft	2,750 kg 6,062 lbs
20' High Cube Dry	5.919 m 19'5"	2.340 m 7'8 1/16"	2.286 m 7'6"	33.0 m3 1,179 cft	1,900 kg 4,189 lbs
20' Open Top	5.919 m 19'5"	2.340 m 7'8 1/16"	2.286 m 7'6"	32.0 m3 1,143 cft	2,177 kg 4,799 lbs
20' Flat Rack	5.935 m 19'5 5/8"	2.398 m 7'10 3/8"	2.327 m 7'7 9/16"	--	2,560 kg 5,643 lbs
40' Standard Dry	12.035 m 39'5 13/16"	2.350 m 7'8 1/2"	2.393 m 7'10 3/16"	67.0 m3 2,393 cft	3,700 kg 8,156 lbs
40' High Cube Dry	12.030 m 39'5 9/16"	2.350 m 7'8 1/2"	2.690 m 8'9 7/8"	76.0 m3 2,714 cft	3,930 kg 8,663 lbs
40' Standard Reefer	11.577 m 37'11 3/4"	2.294 m 7'6 1/4"	2.210 m 7'3"	58.7 m3 2,073 cft	3,950 kg 8,708 lbs
40 High-Cube Reefer	11.577 m 37'11 3/4"	2.294 m 7'6 1/4"	2.509 m 8'2 3/4"	67.0 m3 2,366 cft	3,950 kg 8,708 lbs
40' Flat Rack	12.080 m 39'7 9/16"	2.420 m 7'11 1/4"	2.103 m 6'10 13/16	--	5,480 kg 12,080 lbs
45' High Cube Dry	13.556 m 44'5 11/16"	2.352 m 7'8 9/16"	2.695 m 8'10 1/16"	86.0 m3 3.031 cft	4,590 kg 10.118 lbs

CARGOBID
BASICS

Unit Load Devices

Airfreight uses cargo transport units known as Unit Load Devices (ULD). Many types and shapes of ULD fit the unique requirements of aircraft holds, including refrigerated ULD. All conform to standards established by the International Airline Transport Association (IATA).

ULD come in two common types: containers and pallets. Many cargo aircraft configurations allow a combination of these types with various sizes. The maximum accepted weight (payload) varies by aircraft type and the particular container or pallet build-up. The same goes for pallets volumes. These also vary according to lower deck or main deck loading. The actual dimensions may differ according to the manufacturer or aircraft type.

Below you find the most usual ULD. Your forwarder or carrier is best equipped to assist you in choosing the most suitable ULD for your needs.

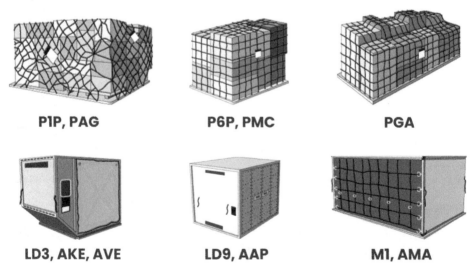

| P1P, PAG | P6P, PMC | PGA |
| LD3, AKE, AVE | LD9, AAP | M1, AMA |

ANNEX 2

HAZARDOUS CARGO

An essential factor to take into account across international supply chains is cargo safety.

The first step in lowering the dangers associated with each cargo is to identify risky products and then properly package, handle, stowage, and communicate them to the relevant parties.

Classification is required to guarantee that items are packaged safely and to convey relevant information to people involved in carriage (transport), emergency services and responders, and end-users, including customers and those at work.

Hazardous cargo training always includes the use of the following classification system. This system covers the most important safety rules and recommendations for packed goods and multimodal shipments.

Class 1 - Explosives

Explosives are materials that can conflagrate or detonate quickly because of chemical reactions. They can cause catastrophic damage through force and/or of producing otherwise hazardous amounts of heat, light, sound, smoke or gas.

Examples: ammunition, fireworks, flares, fuse, detonators, primers, igniters, rockets, air bag inflators, toy caps.

1.1 - Explosives with a mass explosion hazard

Consists of explosives that have a mass explosion hazard. A mass explosion is one that may affect the entire load instantaneously.

Examples: nitroglycerine, dynamite.

1.2 - Explosives with a severe projection hazard

Consists of explosives that have a projection hazard but not a mass explosion hazard.

1.3 - Explosives with a fire

Consists of explosives that have a fire hazard and either a minor blast hazard or a minor projection hazard or both but not a mass explosion hazard.

1.4 - Minor fire or projection hazard

Consists of explosives that present a minor explosion hazard. The explosive effects confine to the package and no projection of fragments of appreciable size or range is to be expected. An external fire must not cause virtually instantaneous explosion of almost the entire contents of the package.

1.5 - Very insensitive blasting agents

Consists of very insensitive explosives with a mass explosion hazard (explosion similar to 1.1). This division comprises substances that have a mass explosion hazard but are so insensitive that there is a weak probability of initiation or of transition from burning to detonation under normal conditions of transport.

1.6 - Extremely insensitive explosives

Consists of extremely insensitive articles that
do not have a mass explosive hazard.
This division is comprised of articles which
contain only extremely insensitive detonating
substances and which show a negligible
probability of accidental initiation or propagation.

Class 2 - Gases

Some gases can pose serious hazards due to their flammability,
potential as asphyxiants, ability to oxidize and/or their toxicity or
corrosiveness to humans. This class includes gases in a
compressed state, liquefied, dissolved, refrigerated liquefied
gases, and mixtures of one or more gases with these
characteristics.

2.1 - Flammable gases

Gases that ignite on contact with an ignition
source, such as acetylene and hydrogen.
Flammable gas means any material that is
ignitable at 101.3 kPa (14.7 psi) when in a
mixture of 13% or less by volume with air, or has
a flammable range at 101.3 kPa (14.7 psi) with
air of at least 12% regardless of the lower limit.
Examples: disposable cigarette lighters and refills for gas
lighters, acetylene (for oxy-acetylene welding and brazing),
ethylene (for ripening fruit) and hydrogen (for university and
industry use).

2.2 - Non-flammable, non-toxic gases

Gases that are neither flammable nor poisonous. Includes the cryogenic gases/liquids (at temperatures below -100 °C) used for cryopreservation and rocket fuels. This division includes compressed gas, liquefied gas, pressurized cryogenic gas, compressed gas
in solution, asphyxiant gas and oxidizing gas. A non-flammable, nonpoisonous compressed gas means any material which exerts in the packaging an absolute pressure of 280 kPa (40.6 psi) or greater at 20 °C (68 °F) and does not meet the definition of subclass 2.1 or 2.3.

Examples: carbon dioxide (found in soft drink dispensing machines), oxygen (for hospitals and oxy-acetylene welding), compressed air, freons (for refrigeration, air conditioning and polyurethane manufacture), compressed nitrogen and argon (for welding). Also, liquid oxygen and liquid nitrogen (for industrial applications).

2.3 - Toxic gases

Gases liable to cause death or serious injury to human health if inhaled. Gas poisonous by inhalation means a material which is a gas at 20 °C or less and a pressure of 101.3 kPa (a material with a boiling point of 20 °C or less at 101.3kPa (14.7 psi)) which is known to be so toxic to humans as to pose a hazard to health during transport. In the absence of adequate data on human toxicity, it may be toxic to humans because when tested on laboratory animals it has an LC50 value of not more than 5000 ml/m3.

Examples: methyl bromide and ethylene oxide (for fumigation), chlorine (for commercial swimming pool water sanitation), ammonia (for industrial freezing works), fluorine, and hydrogen cyanide.
Some aerosols – fly sprays, room fresheners, aerosol deodorants – oven cleaners are assigned to subclasses 2.1 or 2.2 depending on their properties.

Class 3 - Flammable Liquids

A flammable liquid means a liquid that may catch fire easily or any mixture having one or more components with any flash point, i.e. they give off a flammable vapor at temperatures lower than 60-65 °C. It is strongly advised for shipping liquids at or above its flash point in a bulk packaging.

There are three main groups of flammable liquids:

- Low flash point - liquids with a flash point below -18 °C.

- Intermediate flash point - liquids with a flash point from -18 °C up to +23 °C.

- High flash point - liquids with a flash point from +23 °C.

Examples: oil, petrol, diesel, mineral turpentine, kerosene, methylated spirits, enamel paints, car lacquers, polyurethane varnish, two-pot polyurethanes and their solvents, most varnishes and some dry-cleaning fluids, methanol, methyl ethyl ketone (acetone) and polyester resin kit.

Class 4 - Flammable Solids or Substances

4.1 - Flammable solids

Solid substances that are easily ignited. Self-reactive materials, which are thermally unstable and that can undergo a strongly exothermic decomposition even without the presence of air. Readily combustible solids that can cause a fire through friction and show a burning rate faster than 2.2 mm (0.087 inches) per second, or metal powders that can be ignited and react over the whole length of a sample in 10 minutes or less.

Examples: matches, fire lighters, sulphur powder, nitrocellulose, magnesium, synthetic camphor, naphthalene (moth balls).

CARGOBID
BASICS

4.2 - Spontaneously combustible substances

Solid substances that ignite in a spontaneous way. Spontaneously combustible material is a pyrophoric material, which is a liquid or solid that can ignite within five minutes after coming in contact with air or a self-heating material that when in contact with air and without an energy supply is liable to self-heat.

Examples: white or yellow phosphorus, aluminium alkyls, copra and unstabilised fish meal.

4.3 - Dangerous when wet

Solid or liquid substances that emit a flammable gas when wet. They are made of a material that when it makes contact with water it is liable to become spontaneously flammable or give off flammable or toxic gas at a rate greater than 1 L per kilogram of the material per hour.

Examples: calcium, sodium, potassium metals and calcium carbide (used to produce acetylene gas).

Class 5 - Oxidizing substances and organic peroxides

5.1 - Oxidizing agents

Oxidizing agent means a material that may, generally by yielding oxygen, cause or enhance the combustion of other materials.

Examples: calcium hypochlorite, some home bleaches, ammonium nitrate, hydrogen peroxide, potassium permanganate. Products used for stripping printed circuit board.

5.2 - Organic peroxides

Organic peroxides are any organic compounds containing oxygen in the bivalent structure and which may be considered a derivative of hydrogen peroxides, where one or more of the hydrogen atoms have been replaced by organic radicals.

Examples: benzoyl peroxides, cumene hydroperoxide, hardeners used in manufacturing industries.

Class 6 - Toxic and infectious

6.1 - Toxic

Poisonous substances that are able to cause death or serious hazard to humans health.

Examples: pesticides, mercuric chloride, methylene chloride, potassium cyanide, sodium cyanide (for metal treatment).
Several metal degreasers are poisons, such as chromium salts in electroplating and copper chrome arsenate mixtures for timber preservatives.

6.2 - Biohazards

These materials are infectious because they contain pathogens, or, at least, are presumed to do so. Pathogens are microorganisms (including bacteria, viruses, rickettsiae, parasites, fungi) and other agents such as prions, which can cause disease in humans or animals.

Examples: used intravenous needles, blood samples from people with infectious and/or notifiable diseases, septic tank effluent wastes, cultures containing pathogen(s) which may cause infection.

Class 7 - Radioactive substances

Radioactive substances comprise substances or a combination of substances that emit ionizing radiation, such as uranium and plutonium.

Examples: Materials used in industrial thickness measuring devices, for the sterilization of medical products and as a treatment for cancer.

Class 8 - Corrosive Substances

A corrosive material means a liquid or solid that causes full thickness destruction of human skin at the site of contact within a specified period of time. For example, a liquid that has a severe corrosion rate on steel is also a corrosive material.

8.1 - Acids

Examples: hydrochloric acid, sulphuric acid.

8.2 - Alkalis

Examples: sodium hydroxide (caustic soda), potassium hydroxide (caustic potash). Many dairy sanitizers and industrial cleaners are corrosive and belong to this class.

Class 9 - Miscellaneous

A material which presents a hazard during transport but which does not meet the definition of any other hazard class. This class includes any material that has an anesthetic, noxious or other similar property that could cause extreme annoyance or discomfort to a crew member so as to prevent the correct performance of assigned duties, or material for an elevated temperature material, a hazardous substance, a hazardous waste, or a marine pollutant.

Class 9 should not be regarded as presenting a lower risk than Classes 1 to 8.

Examples: blue, brown and white asbestos (cancer hazard), PCBs (environmental and health hazards), some ammonium nitrate fertilizers and environmentally hazardous substances, lithium ion batteries, car batteries, dry ice, self-inflating life rafts.

Segregation

Some substances should not be stowed together in the same container. They should follow separation requirements, a practice known as segregation. When sending dangerous goods, shippers should follow the segregation rules described in the IMDG Code. These should apply not only to the multimodal transport but also to the storage and handling stages.

The following segregation table outlines basic incompatibilities between different classes and subclasses of cargo, whether they can be shipped or not inside the same cargo transportation unit.

CLASS		1.1 1.2 1.5	1.3 1.6	1.4	2.1	2.2	2.3	3	4.1	4.2	4.3	5.1	5.2	6.1	6.2	7	8	9
Explosives	1.1, 1.2, 1.5	Apply rules within Class 1			4	2	2	4	4	4	4	4	4	2	4	2	4	X
Explosives	1.3, 1.6	Apply rules within Class 1			4	2	2	4	3	3	4	4	4	2	4	2	2	X
Explosives	1.4	Apply rules within Class 1			2	1	1	2	2	2	2	2	2	X	4	2	2	X
Flammable gases	2.1	4	4	2	X	X	X	2	1	2	X	2	2	X	4	2	1	X
Non-toxic, non-flammable gases	2.2	2	2	1	X	X	X	1	X	1	X	X	1	X	2	1	X	X
Toxic gases	2.3	2	2	1	X	X	X	2	X	2	X	X	2	X	2	1	X	X
Flammable	3	4	4	2	2	1	2	X	X	2	1	2	2	X	3	2	X	X
Flammable solids (including self-reactive substances and solid desensitized explosives)	4.1	4	3	2	1	X	X	X	X	1	X	1	2	X	3	2	1	X
Substances liable to spontaneous combustion	4.2	4	3	2	2	1	2	2	1	X	1	2	2	1	3	2	1	X
Substances which, in contact with water, emmit flammable gases	4.3	4	4	2	X	X	X	1	X	1	X	2	2	X	2	2	1	X
Oxidizing substances (agents)	5.1	4	4	2	2	X	X	2	1	2	2	X	2	1	3	1	2	X
Organic peroxides	5.2	4	4	2	2	1	2	2	2	2	2	2	X	1	3	2	2	X
Toxic substances	6.1	2	2	X	X	X	X	X	X	1	X	1	1	X	1	X	X	X
Infectious substances	6.2	4	4	4	4	2	2	3	3	3	2	3	3	1	X	X	3	X
Radioactive material	7	2	2	2	2	1	1	2	2	2	2	1	2	X	3	2	2	X
Corrosive substances	8	4	2	2	1	X	X	X	1	1	1	2	2	X	3	2	X	X
Miscellaneous dangerous	9	X	X	X	X	X	X	X	X	X	X	X	X	X	X	X	X	X

Legend

X – YES, they can load in the same container. Please check the IMDG Code for further provisions.
1 – NO, they cannot load in the same container. Keep "away from".
2 – NO, they cannot load in the same container. Keep "separated from".
3 – NO, they cannot load in the same container. Keep "separated by a complete compartment or hold from".
4 – NO, they cannot load in the same container. Keep "separated longitudinally by an intervening complete compartment or hold from"

How to use the segregation table

Suppose a shipper wants to send Class 5.2 organic peroxides with Class 3 flammable liquids in the same container. At the intersection of the respective column and row of each class, there is number 2, which means the two materials should not be carried in the same container and should be placed separated from each other. Only substances of classes marked with intersection X may co-load within the same container.

There are many subsidiary risks that require different and multiple safety provisions. You should always consult the dangerous goods list (DGL) in the IMDG Code for specific details.

The information above is for general reference only. Please ask your carrier for guidance before you arrange for a shipment with dangerous goods.

ANNEX 3

INCOTERMS®

The Incoterms® rules are a set of contractual provisions that can be incorporated into the contracts of sale of goods. They have been developed and maintained by experts brought together by the International Chamber of Commerce (ICC). First published in 1936, the rules are subject to periodical revisions by the ICC to account for changing modes of transport and document delivery. The rules have become the global standard for international trade because they help exporters, importers, insurers, and carriers to avoid costly misunderstandings by clearly defining the responsibilities of sellers and buyers for the delivery of goods. They consist of 3-letter abbreviations for lengthy contract provisions.

Classification of Incoterms® Rules

Incoterms® rules are grouped into four categories.

E term (EXW)
The only rule where the exporter/seller makes the goods available at his/her own premises to the importer/buyer.

F terms (FCA, FAS and FOB)
Rules where the exporter/seller is responsible for delivering the goods to a named carrier by the buyer.

C terms (CFR, CIF, CPT and CIP)
Rules where the exporter/seller is responsible for contracting and paying for carriage of the goods, but not responsible for additional costs or risk of damage or loss to the goods once they have been shipped.

D terms (DPU, DAP and DDP)
Rules where the exporter/seller is responsible for all costs and risks associated with delivering the goods to the place of destination.

Not all Incoterms® rules are adequate for all modes of transport. Some terms were designed specifically for sea vessels while others were meant to be applicable to all modes.
The following are extracts of the 11 rules from the latest Incoterms® 2020 revision. The list is ordered by increasing risk and liability to the exporter/seller.

Rules for any Mode or Modes of Transport

EXW - Ex Works (...named place)

"Ex Works" means that the seller delivers when it places the goods at the disposal of the buyer at the seller's premises or at another named place (i.e., works, factory, warehouse, etc.). The seller does not need to load the goods on any collecting vehicle, nor does it need to clear the goods for export, where such clearance is applicable.

FCA - Free Carrier (...named place)

"Free Carrier" means that the seller delivers the goods to the carrier or another person nominated by the buyer at the seller's premises or another named place. The parties are well advised to specify as clearly as possible the point within the named place of delivery, as the risk passes to the buyer at that point.

CPT - Carriage Paid To (...named place of destination)

"Carriage Paid To" means that the seller delivers the goods to the carrier or another person nominated by the seller at an agreed place (if any such place is agreed between parties) and that the seller must contract for and pay the costs of carriage necessary to bring the goods to the named place of destination.

CARGOBID
BASICS

CIP - Carriage And Insurance Paid To (...named place of destination)

"Carriage and Insurance Paid to" means that the seller delivers the goods to the carrier or another person nominated by the seller at an agreed place (if any such place is agreed between parties) and that the seller must contract for and pay the costs of carriage necessary to bring the goods to the named place of destination. The seller also contracts for insurance cover against the buyer's risk of loss of or damage to the goods during the carriage. The buyer should note that under CIP the seller is required to obtain insurance only on minimum cover. Should the buyer wish to have more insurance protection, it will need either to agree as much expressly with the seller or to make its own extra insurance arrangements.

DAP - Delivered At Place (...named place of destination)

"Delivered at Place" means that the seller delivers when the goods are placed at the disposal of the buyer on the arriving means of transport ready for unloading at the named place of destination. The seller bears all risks involved in bringing the goods to the named place. DAP replaces the earlier Incoterms® DAF, DDU.

DDP - Delivered Duty Paid (...named place of destination)

"Delivered Duty Paid" means that the seller delivers the goods when the goods are placed at the disposal of the buyer, cleared for import on the arriving means of transport ready for unloading at the named place of destination. The seller bears all the costs and risks involved in bringing the goods to the place of destination and is obliged to clear the goods not only for export but also for import, to pay any duty for both export and import and to carry out all customs formalities.

The Incoterms® 2020 revision changed rule DAT into DPU.

Earlier, the 2010 revision had 4 Incoterms® rules dropped: DAF (Delivery at Frontier), DES (Delivery ex-ship), DEQ (Delivery ex-quay) and DDU (Delivery duty unpaid).

Two new rules were introduced back then: DAT - Delivery at Terminal (replaced DEQ) and DAP – Delivery at Place (replaced DAF, DES and DDU).

Rules for Sea and Inland Waterway Transport

FAS - Free Alongside Ship (...named port of shipment)

"Free Alongside Ship" means that the seller delivers when the goods are placed alongside the vessel (e.g., on a quay or a barge) nominated by the buyer at the named port of shipment. The risk of loss of or damage to the goods passes when the goods are alongside the ship, and the buyer bears all costs from that moment onwards.

FOB - Free On Board (...named port of shipment)

"Free On Board" means that the seller delivers the goods on board the vessel nominated by the buyer at the named port of shipment or procures the goods already so delivered. The risk of loss of or damage to the goods passes when the goods are on board the vessel, and the buyer bears all costs from that moment onwards.

CARGOBID
BASICS

CFR - Cost and Freight (...named port of destination)

"Cost and Freight" means that the seller delivers the goods on board the vessel or procures the goods already so delivered. The risk of loss of or damage to the goods passes when the goods are on board the vessel. The seller must contract for and pay the costs and freight necessary to bring the goods to the named port of destination.

CIF - Cost, Insurance and Freight (...named port of destination)

"Cost, Insurance and Freight" means that the seller delivers the goods on board the vessel or procures the goods already so delivered. The risk of loss of or damage to the goods passes when the goods are on board the vessel. The seller must contract for and pay the costs and freight necessary to bring the goods to the named port of destination. The seller also contracts for insurance cover against the buyer's risk of loss of or damage to the goods during the carriage. The buyer should note that under CIF the seller is required to obtain insurance only on minimum cover. Should the buyer wish to have more insurance protection, it will need either to agree as much expressly with the seller or to make its own extra insurance arrangements.

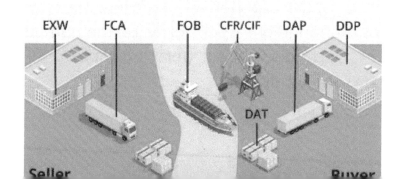

Incoterms

EXW   FCA   FOB   CFR/CIF   DAP   DDP

DAT

Seller   Buyer

Table of the Incoterms® rules
and the responsibilities of each party

Charges/Fees	Any transport mode			Sea/inland waterway transport			Any transport mode				
	EXW	FCA	FAS	FOB	CFR	CIF	CPT	CPI	DPU	DAP	DDP
Packaging	Buyer or Seller	Seller	Seller	Seller	Seller	Seller	Seller	Seller	Seller	Seller	Seller
Loading charges	Buyer	Seller	Seller	Seller	Seller	Seller	Seller	Seller	Seller	Seller	Seller
Delivery to port/place	Buyer	Seller	Seller	Seller	Seller	Seller	Seller	Seller	Seller	Seller	Seller
Export duty & taxes	Buyer	Seller	Seller	Seller	Seller	Seller	Seller	Seller	Seller	Seller	Seller
Origin terminal charges	Buyer	Buyer	Seller	Seller	Seller	Seller	Seller	Seller	Seller	Seller	Seller
Loading on carriage	Buyer	Buyer	Buyer	Seller	Seller	Seller	Seller	Seller	Seller	Seller	Seller
Carriage charges	Buyer	Buyer	Buyer	Buyer	Seller	Seller	Seller	Seller	Seller	Seller	Seller
Insurance						Seller		Seller			
Destination terminal charges	Buyer	Buyer	Buyer	Buyer	Buyer	Buyer	Seller	Seller	Seller	Seller	Seller
Delivery to destination	Buyer	Buyer	Buyer	Buyer	Buyer	Buyer	Buyer	Buyer	Buyer	Seller	Seller
Import duty & charges	Buyer	Buyer	Buyer	Buyer	Buyer	Buyer	Buyer	Buyer	Buyer	Buyer	Seller

Use of Incoterms® rules

Incoterms® rules are not 'laws' and they are not implied into contracts for the sale of goods. It is important for the seller and buyer to agree on the terms of sale and know precisely what is included in the sale price. Exporters should choose the Incoterms® rule that works best for their companies, but also, be prepared to quote on other terms.

While inserting an Incoterms® rule on a quotation or commercial invoice, the exporter should follow the term by the point of exchange of responsibility, i.e. the named place/port of load/discharge (for example "CIF Rotterdam", "FOB Shanghai").

Choose the right Incoterms® rules

The two most popular Incoterms® rules in maritime shipping are CIF and FOB. Many factors influence the most proper term for a given transaction. However, in order for traders to maximize their profits, the rule of thumb is to sell CIF and buy FOB.

Selling on CIF terms allows the exporter to make a slightly higher profit because he/she is able to choose and negotiate the freight services. Buying on FOB terms means the importer can save on costs through the negotiation of better freight deals on importer's end. When it comes to air shipments, FOB is sometimes wrongly assigned, where FCA should be the correct Incoterms® rule to use. A company without experience in international trade, or with a small cargo volume, might prefer to use EXW term because that poses less trouble with a shipment.

FCA is usually the preferred choice for containerised goods. In such case, the seller is forced to leave the cargo at a port terminal, so they can then be loaded using the port loading equipment. FCA Incoterms® establish that the seller should deliver the containers at a location (in this case, the port terminal), and this is when the risk transfers to the buyer, who is responsible for arranging the loading.

Limitations

Incoterms® rules can be useful, but their usage has limitations because they do not convey on their own the full intent of the parties.

You can find more on Incoterms® by visiting the ICC's online bookstore.

What we do at CargoBid

We are aware of the complex relationship between buyers and sellers in the global trade. This sparked CargoBid® — a service founded by people sharing a vision on how to improve the supply chain of importers and exporters around the world.

Our expertise in logistics and our passion for the green economy took us on a quest to improve the purchasing model in the global supply chains. It inspired us to create a B2B platform to promote sustainability while sourcing rates in the freight markets.

Our mission

- Create the world's most respected freight exchange
- Help shippers get freight rates and optimize their purchasing processes
- Help carriers generate sales leads and grow their customer base
- Provide unmatched value for air and sea freight procurement

MEET THE TEAM

Carlos   Partner, Designer

Well seasoned in shipping and logistics, Carlos made freight beautiful at various shipping agencies and freight forwarders. Besides being the cofounder, he heads the customer success experience in our marketplace.

Guido   Partner, Manager

Guido came up with crystalising a logistics startup following his exceptional business management skills. Well versed in IT in the publishing industry, he excels in fostering entrepreneurship to the next level.

Nguyen Sato   Sales & Marketing

A proven track record in real estate brokerage did not prevent Nguyen from joining the ranks of logistics professionals and help build trust in a startup brand devoted to freight exchanges.

Made in the USA
Monee, IL
14 November 2024